PUTTING PEN TO PAPER
IS SAID TO HELP
THE BRAIN
"REGULATE EMOTION"
AND REDUCES
FEELINGS OF ANXIETY,
FEAR AND SADNESS.

MONTHLY PLAN

01 02 03 04 05 06 07 08 09 10 11 12

SUNDAY	MONDAY	TUESDAY

PINKFOOT

WEDNESDAY	THURSDAY	FRIDAY	SATURDAY

WEEKLY PLAN

01 02 03 04

05 06 07 08

09 10 11 12

TO DO LIST

MONDAY

TUESDAY

WEDNESDAY

THURSDAY

FRIDAY

SATURDAY

SUNDAY

PINKFOOT

WEEKLY PLAN

01 02 03 04

05 06 07 08

09 10 11 12

MONDAY

TUESDAY

WEDNESDAY

THURSDAY

FRIDAY

SUNDAY

PINKFOOT

WEEKLY PLAN

01 02 03 04

05 06 07 08

09 10 11 12

TO DO LIST

MONDAY

TUESDAY

WEDNESDAY

THURSDAY

FRIDAY

SATURDAY

SUNDAY

PINKFOOT

WEEKLY PLAN

01	02	03	04
05	06	07	08
09	10	11	12

TO DO LIST

MONDAY

TUESDAY

WEDNESDAY

HURSDAY

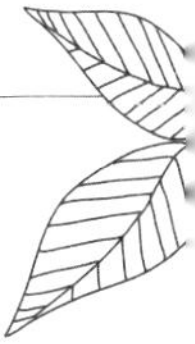

FRIDAY

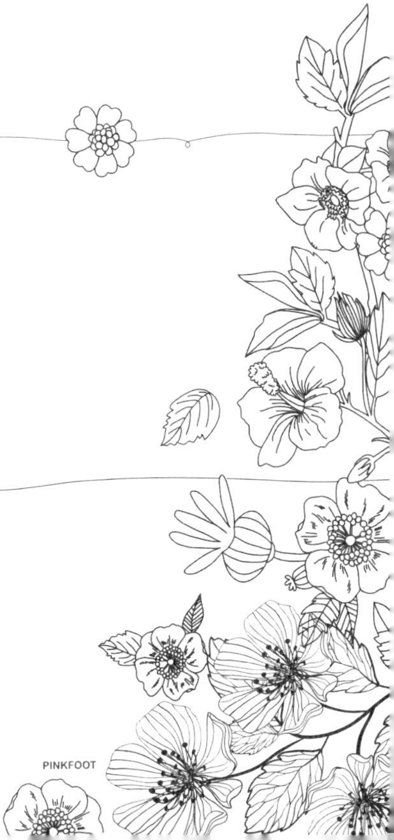

SUNDAY

PINKFOOT

WEEKLY PLAN

01	02	03	04
05	06	07	08
09	10	11	12

TO DO LIST

MONDAY

TUESDAY

WEDNESDAY

THURSDAY

FRIDAY

SATURDAY

SUNDAY

PINKFOOT

ACCOUNT PAGE

DATE	CONTENTS	INCOME	OUTLAY	PAYMENT OPTION	TOTAL
				☐ CASH ☐ CARD	
				☐ CASH ☐ CARD	
				☐ CASH ☐ CARD	
				☐ CASH ☐ CARD	
				☐ CASH ☐ CARD	
				☐ CASH ☐ CARD	
				☐ CASH ☐ CARD	
				☐ CASH ☐ CARD	
				☐ CASH ☐ CARD	
				☐ CASH ☐ CARD	
				☐ CASH ☐ CARD	
				☐ CASH ☐ CARD	
				☐ CASH ☐ CARD	
				☐ CASH ☐ CARD	
				☐ CASH ☐ CARD	
				☐ CASH ☐ CARD	
				☐ CASH ☐ CARD	
				☐ CASH ☐ CARD	
				☐ CASH ☐ CARD	
				☐ CASH ☐ CARD	
				☐ CASH ☐ CARD	

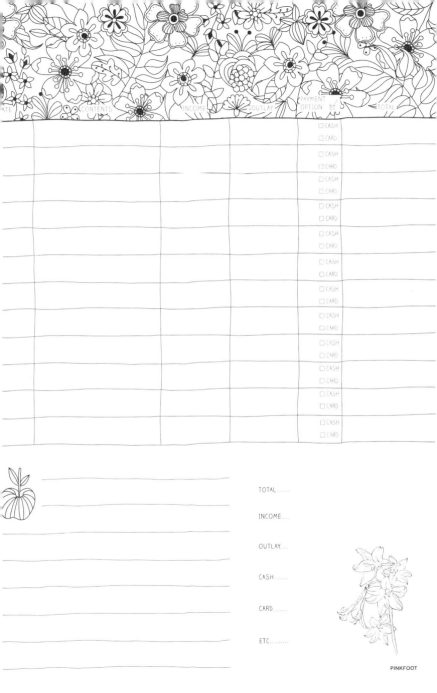

DATE	CONTENTS	INCOME	OUTLAY	PAYMENT OPTION	TOTAL
				☐ CASH ☐ CARD	
				☐ CASH ☐ CARD	
				☐ CASH ☐ CARD	
				☐ CASH ☐ CARD	
				☐ CASH ☐ CARD	
				☐ CASH ☐ CARD	
				☐ CASH ☐ CARD	
				☐ CASH ☐ CARD	
				☐ CASH ☐ CARD	
				☐ CASH ☐ CARD	
				☐ CASH ☐ CARD	
				☐ CASH ☐ CARD	
				☐ CASH ☐ CARD	

TOTAL......

INCOME....

OUTLAY...

CASH......

CARD......

ETC.........

PINKFOOT

CHECK LIST:

DATE	CONTENTS	CHECK	DATE	CONTENTS	CH

PUTTING PEN TO PAPER
IS SAID TO HELP
THE BRAIN
"REGULATE EMOTION"
AND REDUCES
FEELINGS OF ANXIETY,
FEAR AND SADNESS.

MONTHLY PLAN

01 02 03 04 05 06 07 08 09 10 11 12

SUNDAY	MONDAY	TUESDAY

PINKFOOT

WEDNESDAY	THURSDAY	FRIDAY	SATURDAY

WEEKLY PLAN

01 02 03 04

05 06 07 08

09 10 11 12

MONDAY

TUESDAY

WEDNESDAY

THURSDAY

FRIDAY

SATURDAY

SUNDAY

PINKFOOT

WEEKLY PLAN

01 02 03 04

05 06 07 08

09 10 11 12

TO DO LIST

MONDAY

TUESDAY

WEDNESDAY

PINKFOOT

WEEKLY PLAN

01 02 03 04

05 06 07 08

09 10 11 12

MONDAY

TUESDAY

WEDNESDAY

THURSDAY

FRIDAY

SATURDAY

SUNDAY

PINKFOOT

WEEKLY PLAN

01 02 03 04

05 06 07 08

09 10 11 12

MONDAY

TUESDAY

WEDNESDAY

THURSDAY

FRIDAY

SUNDAY

PINKFOOT

WEEKLY PLAN

01 02 03 04
05 06 07 08
09 10 11 12

TO DO LIST

MONDAY

TUESDAY

WEDNESDAY

THURSDAY

FRIDAY

SATURDAY

SUNDAY

PINKFOOT

ACCOUNT PAGE

DATE	CONTENTS	INCOME	OUTLAY	PAYMENT OPTION	TOTAL
				☐ CASH ☐ CARD	
				☐ CASH ☐ CARD	
				☐ CASH ☐ CARD	
				☐ CASH ☐ CARD	
				☐ CASH ☐ CARD	
				☐ CASH ☐ CARD	
				☐ CASH ☐ CARD	
				☐ CASH ☐ CARD	
				☐ CASH ☐ CARD	
				☐ CASH ☐ CARD	
				☐ CASH ☐ CARD	
				☐ CASH ☐ CARD	
				☐ CASH ☐ CARD	
				☐ CASH ☐ CARD	
				☐ CASH ☐ CARD	
				☐ CASH ☐ CARD	
				☐ CASH ☐ CARD	
				☐ CASH ☐ CARD	
				☐ CASH ☐ CARD	
				☐ CASH ☐ CARD	
				☐ CASH ☐ CARD	

TE	CONTENTS	INCOME	OUTLAY	PAYMENT OPTION	TOTAL
				☐ CASH / ☐ CARD	
				☐ CASH / ☐ CARD	
				☐ CASH / ☐ CARD	
				☐ CASH / ☐ CARD	
				☐ CASH / ☐ CARD	
				☐ CASH / ☐ CARD	
				☐ CASH / ☐ CARD	
				☐ CASH / ☐ CARD	
				☐ CASH / ☐ CARD	
				☐ CASH / ☐ CARD	
				☐ CASH / ☐ CARD	
				☐ CASH / ☐ CARD	
				☐ CASH / ☐ CARD	
				☐ CASH / ☐ CARD	

TOTAL......

INCOME....

OUTLAY....

CASH.......

CARD........

ETC..........

PINKFOOT

CHECK LIST

DATE	CONTENTS	CHECK	DATE	CONTENTS	C

PUTTING PEN TO PAPER
IS SAID TO HELP
THE BRAIN
"REGULATE EMOTION"
AND REDUCES
FEELINGS OF ANXIETY,
FEAR AND SADNESS.

MONTHLY PLAN

01 02 03 04 05 06 07 08 09 10 11 12

SUNDAY	MONDAY	TUESDAY

PINKFOOT

WEDNESDAY	THURSDAY	FRIDAY	SATURDAY

WEEKLY PLAN

01	02	03	04
05	06	07	08
09	10	11	12

TO DO LIST

MONDAY

TUESDAY

WEDNESDAY

THURSDAY

FRIDAY

SATURDAY

SUNDAY

PINKFOOT

WEEKLY PLAN

01 02 03 04

05 06 07 08

09 10 11 12

TO DO LIST

MONDAY

TUESDAY

WEDNESDAY

THURSDAY

FRIDAY

SUNDAY

PINKFOOT

WEEKLY PLAN

01 02 03 04

05 06 07 08

09 10 11 12

MONDAY

TUESDAY

WEDNESDAY

HURSDAY

FRIDAY

SATURDAY

SUNDAY

PINKFOOT

TO DO LIST

WEEKLY PLAN

01 02 03 04

05 06 07 08

09 10 11 12

MONDAY

TUESDAY

WEDNESDAY

FRIDAY

SUNDAY

PINKFOOT

TO DO LIST

WEEKLY PLAN

01 02 03 04

05 06 07 08

09 10 11 12

MONDAY

TUESDAY

WEDNESDAY

THURSDAY

FRIDAY

SATURDAY

SUNDAY

PINKFOOT

ACCOUNT PAGE

DATE	CONTENTS	INCOME	OUTLAY	PAYMENT OPTION ☑	TOTAL
				☐ CASH / ☐ CARD	
				☐ CASH / ☐ CARD	
				☐ CASH / ☐ CARD	
				☐ CASH / ☐ CARD	
				☐ CASH / ☐ CARD	
				☐ CASH / ☐ CARD	
				☐ CASH / ☐ CARD	
				☐ CASH / ☐ CARD	
				☐ CASH / ☐ CARD	
				☐ CASH / ☐ CARD	
				☐ CASH / ☐ CARD	
				☐ CASH / ☐ CARD	
				☐ CASH / ☐ CARD	
				☐ CASH / ☐ CARD	
				☐ CASH / ☐ CARD	
				☐ CASH / ☐ CARD	
				☐ CASH / ☐ CARD	
				☐ CASH / ☐ CARD	
				☐ CASH / ☐ CARD	
				☐ CASH / ☐ CARD	
				☐ CASH / ☐ CARD	
				☐ CASH / ☐ CARD	

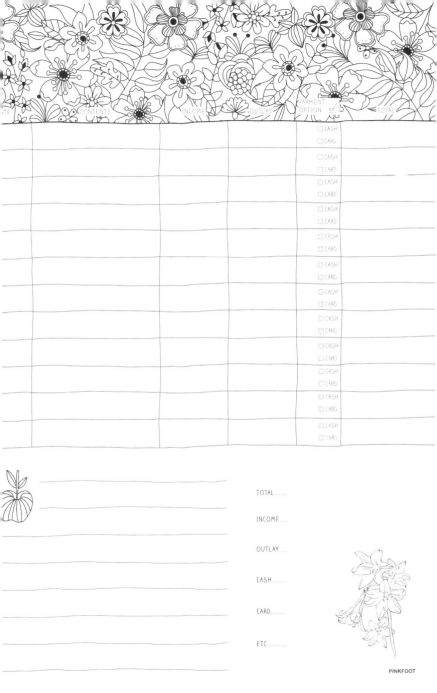

DATE	CONTENTS	INCOME	OUTLAY	PAYMENT OPTION	TOTAL
				☐ CASH ☐ CARD	
				☐ CASH ☐ CARD	
				☐ CASH ☐ CARD	
				☐ CASH ☐ CARD	
				☐ CASH ☐ CARD	
				☐ CASH ☐ CARD	
				☐ CASH ☐ CARD	
				☐ CASH ☐ CARD	
				☐ CASH ☐ CARD	
				☐ CASH ☐ CARD	
				☐ CASH ☐ CARD	
				☐ CASH ☐ CARD	
				☐ CASH ☐ CARD	

TOTAL......

INCOME....

OUTLAY...

CASH......

CARD......

ETC.........

PINKFOOT

CHECK LIST:

DATE	CONTENTS	CHECK	DATE	CONTENTS	CH

PUTTING PEN TO PAPER
IS SAID TO HELP
THE BRAIN
"REGULATE EMOTION"
AND REDUCES
FEELINGS OF ANXIETY,
FEAR AND SADNESS

MONTHLY PLAN

01 02 03 04 05 06 07 08 09 10 11 12

SUNDAY	MONDAY	TUESDAY

PINKFOOT

WEDNESDAY	THURSDAY	FRIDAY	SATURDAY

WEEKLY PLAN

01 02 03 04
05 06 07 08
09 10 11 12

TO DO LIST

MONDAY

TUESDAY

WEDNESDAY

PINKFOOT

WEEKLY PLAN

01 02 03 04

05 06 07 08

09 10 11 12

MONDAY

TUESDAY

WEDNESDAY

WEEKLY PLAN

01	02	03	04
05	06	07	08
09	10	11	12

TO DO LIST

MONDAY

TUESDAY

WEDNESDAY

THURSDAY

FRIDAY

SATURDAY

SUNDAY

PINKFOOT

WEEKLY PLAN

01 02 03 04
05 06 07 08
09 10 11 12

TO DO LIST

MONDAY

TUESDAY

WEDNESDAY

THURSDAY

FRIDAY

SUNDAY

PINKFOOT

WEEKLY PLAN

01 02 03 04

05 06 07 08

09 10 11 12

TO DO LIST

MONDAY

TUESDAY

WEDNESDAY

THURSDAY

FRIDAY

SATURDAY

SUNDAY

PINKFOOT

ACCOUNT PAGE

DATE	CONTENTS	INCOME	OUTLAY	PAYMENT OPTION	TOTAL
				☐ CASH ☐ CARD	
				☐ CASH ☐ CARD	
				☐ CASH ☐ CARD	
				☐ CASH ☐ CARD	
				☐ CASH ☐ CARD	
				☐ CASH ☐ CARD	
				☐ CASH ☐ CARD	
				☐ CASH ☐ CARD	
				☐ CASH ☐ CARD	
				☐ CASH ☐ CARD	
				☐ CASH ☐ CARD	
				☐ CASH ☐ CARD	
				☐ CASH ☐ CARD	
				☐ CASH ☐ CARD	
				☐ CASH ☐ CARD	
				☐ CASH ☐ CARD	
				☐ CASH ☐ CARD	
				☐ CASH ☐ CARD	
				☐ CASH ☐ CARD	
				☐ CASH ☐ CARD	
				☐ CASH ☐ CARD	
				☐ CASH ☐ CARD	
				☐ CASH ☐ CARD	
				☐ CASH ☐ CARD	

DATE	CONTENTS	INCOME	OUTLAY	PAYMENT OPTION ☑		TOTAL
				☐ CASH		
				☐ CARD		
				☐ CASH		
				☐ CARD		
				☐ CASH		
				☐ CARD		
				☐ CASH		
				☐ CARD		
				☐ CASH		
				☐ CARD		
				☐ CASH		
				☐ CARD		
				☐ CASH		
				☐ CARD		
				☐ CASH		
				☐ CARD		
				☐ CASH		
				☐ CARD		
				☐ CASH		
				☐ CARD		
				☐ CASH		
				☐ CARD		
				☐ CASH		
				☐ CARD		

TOTAL......

INCOME....

OUTLAY...

CASH........

CARD.......

ETC..........

PINKFOOT

CHECK LIST

DATE	CONTENTS	CHECK	DATE	CONTENTS	C

PUTTING PEN TO PAPER

IS SAID TO HELP

THE BRAIN

"REGULATE EMOTION"

AND REDUCES

FEELINGS OF ANXIETY,

FEAR AND SADNESS.

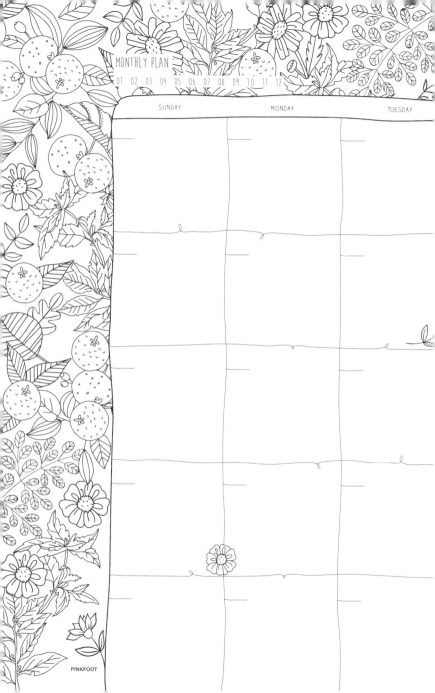

MONTHLY PLAN

01 02 03 04 05 06 07 08 09 10 11 12

SUNDAY	MONDAY	TUESDAY

PINKFOOT

| WEDNESDAY | THURSDAY | FRIDAY | SATURDAY |

WEEKLY PLAN

01 02 03 04

05 06 07 08

09 10 11 12

TO DO LIST

MONDAY

TUESDAY

WEDNESDAY

THURSDAY

FRIDAY

SATURDAY

SUNDAY

PINKFOOT

WEEKLY PLAN

01	02	03	04
05	06	07	08
09	10	11	12

TO DO LIST

MONDAY

TUESDAY

WEDNESDAY

PINKFOOT

WEEKLY PLAN

01   02   03   04

05   06   07   08

09   10   11   12

TO DO LIST

MONDAY

TUESDAY

WEDNESDAY

THURSDAY

FRIDAY

SATURDAY

SUNDAY

PINKFOOT

TO DO LIST

WEEKLY PLAN

01 02 03 04

05 06 07 08

09 10 11 12

MONDAY

TUESDAY

WEDNESDAY

PINKFOOT

WEEKLY PLAN

01	02	03	04
05	06	07	08
09	10	11	12

TO DO LIST

MONDAY

TUESDAY

WEDNESDAY

THURSDAY

FRIDAY

SATURDAY

SUNDAY

PINKFOOT

ACCOUNT PAGE

DATE	CONTENTS	INCOME	OUTLAY	PAYMENT OPTION	TOTAL
				☐ CASH ☐ CARD	
				☐ CASH ☐ CARD	
				☐ CASH ☐ CARD	
				☐ CASH ☐ CARD	
				☐ CASH ☐ CARD	
				☐ CASH ☐ CARD	
				☐ CASH ☐ CARD	
				☐ CASH ☐ CARD	
				☐ CASH ☐ CARD	
				☐ CASH ☐ CARD	
				☐ CASH ☐ CARD	
				☐ CASH ☐ CARD	
				☐ CASH ☐ CARD	
				☐ CASH ☐ CARD	
				☐ CASH ☐ CARD	
				☐ CASH ☐ CARD	
				☐ CASH ☐ CARD	
				☐ CASH ☐ CARD	
				☐ CASH ☐ CARD	
				☐ CASH ☐ CARD	
				☐ CASH ☐ CARD	
				☐ CASH ☐ CARD	

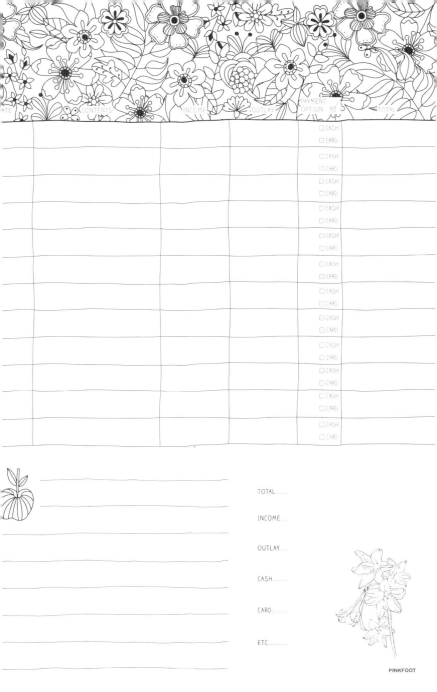

DATE	CONTENTS	INCOME	OUTLAY	PAYMENT OPTION	TOTAL
				☐ CASH / ☐ CARD	
				☐ CASH / ☐ CARD	
				☐ CASH / ☐ CARD	
				☐ CASH / ☐ CARD	
				☐ CASH / ☐ CARD	
				☐ CASH / ☐ CARD	
				☐ CASH / ☐ CARD	
				☐ CASH / ☐ CARD	
				☐ CASH / ☐ CARD	
				☐ CASH / ☐ CARD	
				☐ CASH / ☐ CARD	
				☐ CASH / ☐ CARD	
				☐ CASH / ☐ CARD	

TOTAL......

INCOME....

OUTLAY....

CASH........

CARD.......

ETC..........

CHECK LIST:

DATE	CONTENTS	CHECK	DATE	CONTENTS	CH

PUTTING PEN TO PAPER
IS SAID TO HELP
THE BRAIN
"REGULATE EMOTION"
AND REDUCES
FEELINGS OF ANXIETY,
FEAR AND SADNESS.

MONTHLY PLAN

01 02 03 04 05 06 07 08 09 10 11 12

SUNDAY	MONDAY	TUESDAY

PINKFOOT

WEDNESDAY	THURSDAY	FRIDAY	SATURDAY

WEEKLY PLAN

01 02 03 04

05 06 07 08

09 10 11 12

TO DO LIST

MONDAY

TUESDAY

WEDNESDAY

PINKFOOT

WEEKLY PLAN

01	02	03	04
05	06	07	08
09	10	11	12

TO DO LIST

MONDAY

TUESDAY

WEDNESDAY

THURSDAY

FRIDAY

SUNDAY

WEEKLY PLAN

01 02 03 04

05 06 07 08

09 10 11 12

TO DO LIST

MONDAY

TUESDAY

WEDNESDAY

THURSDAY

FRIDAY

SATURDAY

SUNDAY

PINKFOOT

TO DO LIST

WEEKLY PLAN

01 02 03 04

05 06 07 08

09 10 11 12

MONDAY

TUESDAY

WEDNESDAY

THURSDAY

FRIDAY

SUNDAY

PINKFOOT

TO DO LIST

WEEKLY PLAN

01 02 03 04

05 06 07 08

09 10 11 12

MONDAY

TUESDAY

WEDNESDAY

THURSDAY

FRIDAY

SATURDAY

SUNDAY

PINKFOOT

ACCOUNT PAGE

DATE	CONTENTS	INCOME	OUTLAY	PAYMENT OPTION	TOTAL
				☐ CASH ☐ CARD	
				☐ CASH ☐ CARD	
				☐ CASH ☐ CARD	
				☐ CASH ☐ CARD	
				☐ CASH ☐ CARD	
				☐ CASH ☐ CARD	
				☐ CASH ☐ CARD	
				☐ CASH ☐ CARD	
				☐ CASH ☐ CARD	
				☐ CASH ☐ CARD	
				☐ CASH ☐ CARD	
				☐ CASH ☐ CARD	
				☐ CASH ☐ CARD	
				☐ CASH ☐ CARD	
				☐ CASH ☐ CARD	
				☐ CASH ☐ CARD	
				☐ CASH ☐ CARD	
				☐ CASH ☐ CARD	
				☐ CASH ☐ CARD	
				☐ CASH ☐ CARD	
				☐ CASH ☐ CARD	

DATE	CONTENTS	INCOME	OUTLAY	PAYMENT OPTION	TOTAL
				☐ CASH ☐ CARD	
				☐ CASH ☐ CARD	
				☐ CASH ☐ CARD	
				☐ CASH ☐ CARD	
				☐ CASH ☐ CARD	
				☐ CASH ☐ CARD	
				☐ CASH ☐ CARD	
				☐ CASH ☐ CARD	
				☐ CASH ☐ CARD	
				☐ CASH ☐ CARD	
				☐ CASH ☐ CARD	
				☐ CASH ☐ CARD	
				☐ CASH ☐ CARD	

TOTAL.......

INCOME.....

OUTLAY....

CASH.......

CARD.......

ETC..........

PINKFOOT

DATE	CONTENTS	CHECK	DATE	CONTENTS

PUTTING PEN TO PAPER

IS SAID TO HELP

THE BRAIN

"REGULATE EMOTION"

AND REDUCES

FEELINGS OF ANXIETY,

FEAR AND SADNESS.

MONTHLY PLAN

01 02 03 04 05 06 07 08 09 10 11 12

SUNDAY	MONDAY	TUESDAY

PINKFOOT

WEDNESDAY	THURSDAY	FRIDAY	SATURDAY

WEEKLY PLAN

01 02 03 04

05 06 07 08

09 10 11 12

TO DO LIST

MONDAY

TUESDAY

WEDNESDAY

THURSDAY

FRIDAY

SATURDAY

SUNDAY

PINKFOOT

WEEKLY PLAN

01	02	03	04
05	06	07	08
09	10	11	12

TO DO LIST

MONDAY

TUESDAY

WEDNESDAY

PINKFOOT

WEEKLY PLAN

01 02 03 04

05 06 07 08

09 10 11 12

TO DO LIST

MONDAY

TUESDAY

WEDNESDAY

THURSDAY

FRIDAY

SATURDAY

SUNDAY

PINKFOOT

WEEKLY PLAN

01 02 03 04

05 06 07 08

09 10 11 12

MONDAY

TUESDAY

WEDNESDAY

PINKFOOT

WEEKLY PLAN

01 02 03 04

05 06 07 08

09 10 11 12

MONDAY

TUESDAY

WEDNESDAY

THURSDAY

FRIDAY

SATURDAY

SUNDAY

PINKFOOT

ACCOUNT PAGE

DATE	CONTENTS	INCOME	OUTLAY	PAYMENT OPTION ☑	TOTAL
				☐ CASH ☐ CARD	
				☐ CASH ☐ CARD	
				☐ CASH ☐ CARD	
				☐ CASH ☐ CARD	
				☐ CASH ☐ CARD	
				☐ CASH ☐ CARD	
				☐ CASH ☐ CARD	
				☐ CASH ☐ CARD	
				☐ CASH ☐ CARD	
				☐ CASH ☐ CARD	
				☐ CASH ☐ CARD	
				☐ CASH ☐ CARD	
				☐ CASH ☐ CARD	
				☐ CASH ☐ CARD	
				☐ CASH ☐ CARD	
				☐ CASH ☐ CARD	
				☐ CASH ☐ CARD	
				☐ CASH ☐ CARD	
				☐ CASH ☐ CARD	
				☐ CASH ☐ CARD	
				☐ CASH ☐ CARD	

DATE	CONTENTS	INCOME	OUTLAY	PAYMENT OPTION	TOTAL
				☐ CASH ☐ CARD	
				☐ CASH ☐ CARD	
				☐ CASH ☐ CARD	
				☐ CASH ☐ CARD	
				☐ CASH ☐ CARD	
				☐ CASH ☐ CARD	
				☐ CASH ☐ CARD	
				☐ CASH ☐ CARD	
				☐ CASH ☐ CARD	
				☐ CASH ☐ CARD	
				☐ CASH ☐ CARD	
				☐ CASH ☐ CARD	
				☐ CASH ☐ CARD	

TOTAL......

INCOME....

OUTLAY....

CASH.......

CARD.......

ETC..........

PINKFOOT

CHECK LIST:

DATE	CONTENTS	CHECK	DATE	CONTENTS	CH

PUTTING PEN TO PAPER
IS SAID TO HELP
THE BRAIN
"REGULATE EMOTION"
AND REDUCES
FEELINGS OF ANXIETY,
FEAR AND SADNESS

MONTHLY PLAN

01 02 03 04 05 06 07 08 09 10 11 12

SUNDAY	MONDAY	TUESDAY

PINKFOOT

WEDNESDAY	THURSDAY	FRIDAY	SATURDAY

WEEKLY PLAN

01 02 03 04

05 06 07 08

09 10 11 12

MONDAY

TUESDAY

WEDNESDAY

PINKFOOT

WEEKLY PLAN

01 02 03 04
05 06 07 08
09 10 11 12

TO DO LIST

MONDAY

TUESDAY

WEDNESDAY

THURSDAY

FRIDAY

SATURDAY

SUNDAY

WEEKLY PLAN

01 02 03 04
05 06 07 08
09 10 11 12

MONDAY

TUESDAY

WEDNESDAY

THURSDAY

FRIDAY

SATURDAY

SUNDAY

PINKFOOT

WEEKLY PLAN

01 02 03 04

05 06 07 08

09 10 11 12

MONDAY

TUESDAY

WEDNESDAY

THURSDAY

FRIDAY

SATURDAY

SUNDAY

PINKFOOT

TO DO LIST

WEEKLY PLAN

01 02 03 04

05 06 07 08

09 10 11 12

MONDAY

TUESDAY

WEDNESDAY

THURSDAY

FRIDAY

SATURDAY

SUNDAY

PINKFOOT

ACCOUNT PAGE

DATE	CONTENTS	INCOME	OUTLAY	PAYMENT OPTION	TOTAL
				☐ CASH ☐ CARD	
				☐ CASH ☐ CARD	
				☐ CASH ☐ CARD	
				☐ CASH ☐ CARD	
				☐ CASH ☐ CARD	
				☐ CASH ☐ CARD	
				☐ CASH ☐ CARD	
				☐ CASH ☐ CARD	
				☐ CASH ☐ CARD	
				☐ CASH ☐ CARD	
				☐ CASH ☐ CARD	
				☐ CASH ☐ CARD	
				☐ CASH ☐ CARD	
				☐ CASH ☐ CARD	
				☐ CASH ☐ CARD	
				☐ CASH ☐ CARD	
				☐ CASH ☐ CARD	
				☐ CASH ☐ CARD	
				☐ CASH ☐ CARD	
				☐ CASH ☐ CARD	

CONTENTS	INCOME	OUTLAY	PAYMENT OPTION	TOTAL
			☐ CASH ☐ CARD	
			☐ CASH ☐ CARD	
			☐ CASH ☐ CARD	
			☐ CASH ☐ CARD	
			☐ CASH ☐ CARD	
			☐ CASH ☐ CARD	
			☐ CASH ☐ CARD	
			☐ CASH ☐ CARD	
			☐ CASH ☐ CARD	
			☐ CASH ☐ CARD	
			☐ CASH ☐ CARD	
			☐ CASH ☐ CARD	

TOTAL......

INCOME....

OUTLAY...

CASH......

CARD......

ETC........

PINKFOOT

CHECK LIST

DATE | CONTENTS | CHECK | DATE | CONTENTS | C

PUTTING PEN TO PAPER
IS SAID TO HELP
THE BRAIN
"REGULATE EMOTION"
AND REDUCES
FEELINGS OF ANXIETY,
FEAR AND SADNESS.

MONTHLY PLAN

01 02 03 04 05 06 07 08 09 10 11 12

SUNDAY	MONDAY	TUESDAY

PINKFOOT

WEDNESDAY	THURSDAY	FRIDAY	SATURDAY

WEEKLY PLAN

01	02	03	04
05	06	07	08
09	10	11	12

TO DO LIST

MONDAY

TUESDAY

WEDNESDAY

THURSDAY

FRIDAY

SATURDAY

SUNDAY

PINKFOOT

WEEKLY PLAN

01	02	03	04
05	06	07	08
09	10	11	12

TO DO LIST

MONDAY

TUESDAY

WEDNESDAY

THURSDAY

FRIDAY

SUNDAY

PINKFOOT

WEEKLY PLAN

01	02	03	04
05	06	07	08
09	10	11	12

TO DO LIST

MONDAY

TUESDAY

WEDNESDAY

HURSDAY

FRIDAY

SATURDAY

SUNDAY

PINKFOOT

WEEKLY PLAN

01	02	03	04
05	06	07	08
09	10	11	12

TO DO LIST

MONDAY

TUESDAY

WEDNESDAY

HURSDAY

FRIDAY

SUNDAY

PINKFOOT

WEEKLY PLAN

01 02 03 04
05 06 07 08
09 10 11 12

TO DO LIST

MONDAY

TUESDAY

WEDNESDAY

PINKFOOT

ACCOUNT PAGE

DATE	CONTENTS	INCOME	OUTLAY	PAYMENT OPTION	TOTAL
				☐ CASH ☐ CARD	
				☐ CASH ☐ CARD	
				☐ CASH ☐ CARD	
				☐ CASH ☐ CARD	
				☐ CASH ☐ CARD	
				☐ CASH ☐ CARD	
				☐ CASH ☐ CARD	
				☐ CASH ☐ CARD	
				☐ CASH ☐ CARD	
				☐ CASH ☐ CARD	
				☐ CASH ☐ CARD	
				☐ CASH ☐ CARD	
				☐ CASH ☐ CARD	
				☐ CASH ☐ CARD	
				☐ CASH ☐ CARD	
				☐ CASH ☐ CARD	
				☐ CASH ☐ CARD	
				☐ CASH ☐ CARD	
				☐ CASH ☐ CARD	
				☐ CASH ☐ CARD	
				☐ CASH ☐ CARD	

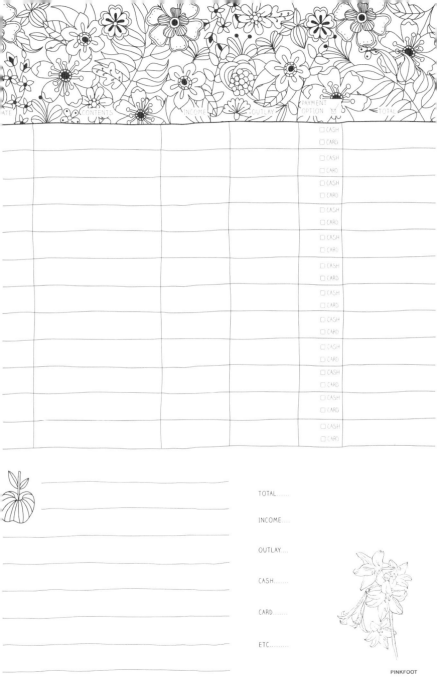

DATE	CONTENTS	INCOME	OUTLAY	PAYMENT OPTION	TOTAL
				☐ CASH ☐ CARD	
				☐ CASH ☐ CARD	
				☐ CASH ☐ CARD	
				☐ CASH ☐ CARD	
				☐ CASH ☐ CARD	
				☐ CASH ☐ CARD	
				☐ CASH ☐ CARD	
				☐ CASH ☐ CARD	
				☐ CASH ☐ CARD	
				☐ CASH ☐ CARD	
				☐ CASH ☐ CARD	

TOTAL......

INCOME....

OUTLAY....

CASH.......

CARD.......

ETC..........

PINKFOOT

CHECK LIST:

DATE	CONTENTS	CHECK	DATE	CONTENTS	CH

PUTTING PEN TO PAPER
IS SAID TO HELP
THE BRAIN
"REGULATE EMOTION"
AND REDUCES
FEELINGS OF ANXIETY,
FEAR AND SADNESS

MONTHLY PLAN

01 02 03 04 05 06 07 08 09 10 11 12

SUNDAY	MONDAY	TUESDAY

PINKFOOT

WEEKLY PLAN

01 02 03 04

05 06 07 08

09 10 11 12

TO DO LIST

MONDAY

TUESDAY

WEDNESDAY

PINKFOOT

WEEKLY PLAN

01 02 03 04
05 06 07 08
09 10 11 12

TO DO LIST

MONDAY

TUESDAY

WEDNESDAY

THURSDAY

FRIDAY

SUNDAY

WEEKLY PLAN

01 02 03 04
05 06 07 08
09 10 11 12

TO DO LIST

MONDAY

TUESDAY

WEDNESDAY

HURSDAY

FRIDAY

SATURDAY

SUNDAY

WEEKLY PLAN

01 02 03 04

05 06 07 08

09 10 11 12

TO DO LIST

MONDAY

TUESDAY

WEDNESDAY

PINKFOOT

WEEKLY PLAN

01 02 03 04
05 06 07 08
09 10 11 12

MONDAY

TUESDAY

WEDNESDAY

THURSDAY

FRIDAY

SATURDAY

SUNDAY

PINKFOOT

ACCOUNT PAGE

DATE	CONTENTS	INCOME	OUTLAY	PAYMENT OPTION	TOTAL
				☐ CASH ☐ CARD	
				☐ CASH ☐ CARD	
				☐ CASH ☐ CARD	
				☐ CASH ☐ CARD	
				☐ CASH ☐ CARD	
				☐ CASH ☐ CARD	
				☐ CASH ☐ CARD	
				☐ CASH ☐ CARD	
				☐ CASH ☐ CARD	
				☐ CASH ☐ CARD	
				☐ CASH ☐ CARD	
				☐ CASH ☐ CARD	
				☐ CASH ☐ CARD	
				☐ CASH ☐ CARD	
				☐ CASH ☐ CARD	
				☐ CASH ☐ CARD	
				☐ CASH ☐ CARD	
				☐ CASH ☐ CARD	
				☐ CASH ☐ CARD	
				☐ CASH ☐ CARD	
				☐ CASH ☐ CARD	

	CONTENTS	INCOME	OUTLAY	PAYMENT OPTION	TOTAL
				☐ CASH ☐ CARD	
				☐ CASH ☐ CARD	
				☐ CASH ☐ CARD	
				☐ CASH ☐ CARD	
				☐ CASH ☐ CARD	
				☐ CASH ☐ CARD	
				☐ CASH ☐ CARD	
				☐ CASH ☐ CARD	
				☐ CASH ☐ CARD	
				☐ CASH ☐ CARD	
				☐ CASH ☐ CARD	
				☐ CASH ☐ CARD	
				☐ CASH ☐ CARD	

TOTAL......

INCOME....

OUTLAY...

CASH........

CARD........

ETC..........

PINKFOOT

CHECK LIST

DATE | CONTENTS | CHECK | DATE | CONTENTS | CH

PUTTING PEN TO PAPER
IS SAID TO HELP
THE BRAIN
"REGULATE EMOTION"
AND REDUCES
FEELINGS OF ANXIETY,
FEAR AND SADNESS

MONTHLY PLAN

01 02 03 04 05 06 07 08 09 10 11 12

SUNDAY	MONDAY	TUESDAY

PINKFOOT

| WEDNESDAY | THURSDAY | FRIDAY | SATURDAY |

WEEKLY PLAN

01	02	03	04
05	06	07	08
09	10	11	12

TO DO LIST

MONDAY

TUESDAY

WEDNESDAY

THURSDAY

FRIDAY

SUNDAY

PINKFOOT

WEEKLY PLAN

01	02	03	04
05	06	07	08
09	10	11	12

TO DO LIST

MONDAY

TUESDAY

WEDNESDAY

PINKFOOT

TO DO LIST

WEEKLY PLAN

01 02 03 04

05 06 07 08

09 10 11 12

MONDAY

TUESDAY

WEDNESDAY

ATURDAY

PINKFOOT

WEEKLY PLAN

01	02	03	04
05	06	07	08
09	10	11	12

TO DO LIST

MONDAY

TUESDAY

WEDNESDAY

PINKFOOT

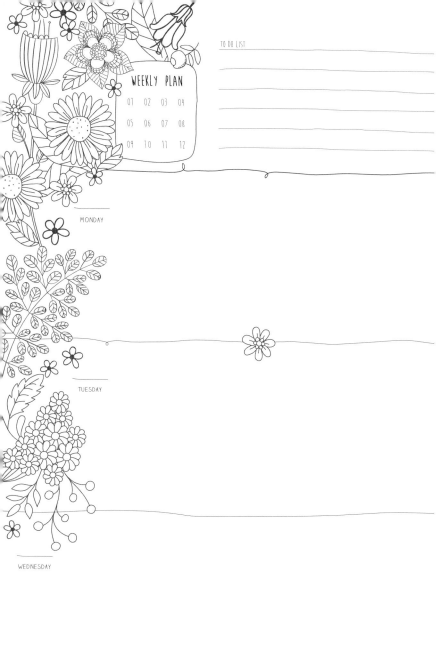

WEEKLY PLAN

01	02	03	04
05	06	07	08
09	10	11	12

TO DO LIST

MONDAY

TUESDAY

WEDNESDAY

THURSDAY

FRIDAY

SATURDAY

SUNDAY

PINKFOOT

ACCOUNT PAGE

DATE	CONTENTS	INCOME	OUTLAY	PAYMENT OPTION	TOTAL
				☐ CASH ☐ CARD	
				☐ CASH ☐ CARD	
				☐ CASH ☐ CARD	
				☐ CASH ☐ CARD	
				☐ CASH ☐ CARD	
				☐ CASH ☐ CARD	
				☐ CASH ☐ CARD	
				☐ CASH ☐ CARD	
				☐ CASH ☐ CARD	
				☐ CASH ☐ CARD	
				☐ CASH ☐ CARD	
				☐ CASH ☐ CARD	
				☐ CASH ☐ CARD	
				☐ CASH ☐ CARD	
				☐ CASH ☐ CARD	
				☐ CASH ☐ CARD	
				☐ CASH ☐ CARD	
				☐ CASH ☐ CARD	
				☐ CASH ☐ CARD	
				☐ CASH ☐ CARD	

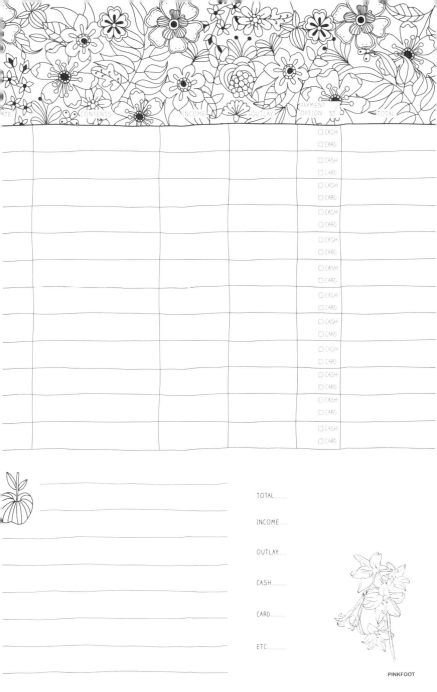

DATE	CONTENTS	INCOME	OUTLAY	PAYMENT OPTION ☑	TOTAL
				☐ CASH ☐ CARD	
				☐ CASH ☐ CARD	
				☐ CASH ☐ CARD	
				☐ CASH ☐ CARD	
				☐ CASH ☐ CARD	
				☐ CASH ☐ CARD	
				☐ CASH ☐ CARD	
				☐ CASH ☐ CARD	
				☐ CASH ☐ CARD	
				☐ CASH ☐ CARD	
				☐ CASH ☐ CARD	
				☐ CASH ☐ CARD	

TOTAL......

INCOME....

OUTLAY....

CASH.......

CARD.......

ETC.........

PINKFOOT

CHECK LIST:

DATE	CONTENTS	CHECK	DATE	CONTENTS	CH

PUTTING PEN TO PAPER

IS SAID TO HELP

THE BRAIN

"REGULATE EMOTION"

AND REDUCES

FEELINGS OF ANXIETY,

FEAR AND SADNESS

MONTHLY PLAN

01 02 03 04 05 06 07 08 09 10 11 12

SUNDAY	MONDAY	TUESDAY

PINKFOOT

WEDNESDAY	THURSDAY	FRIDAY	SATURDAY

WEEKLY PLAN

01 02 03 04

05 06 07 08

09 10 11 12

TO DO LIST

MONDAY

TUESDAY

WEDNESDAY

THURSDAY

FRIDAY

SATURDAY

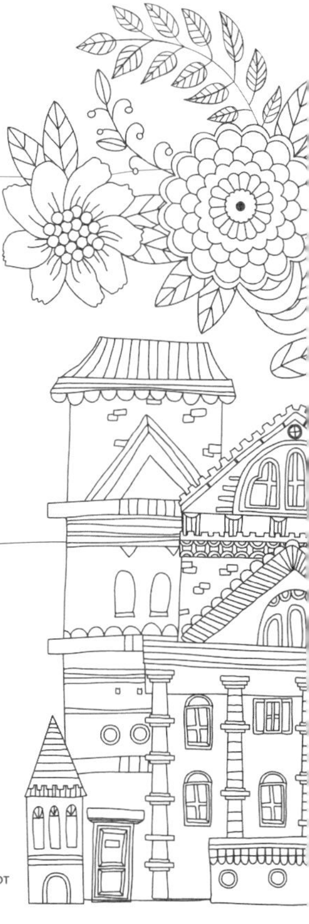

SUNDAY

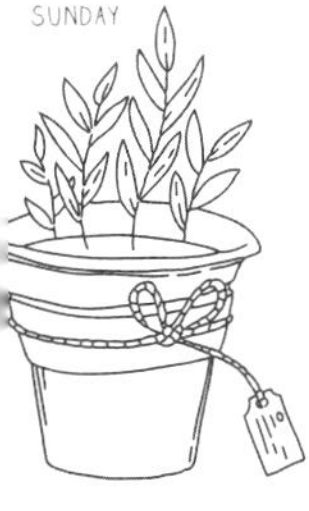

PINKFOOT

WEEKLY PLAN

01 02 03 04

05 06 07 08

09 10 11 12

TO DO LIST

MONDAY

TUESDAY

WEDNESDAY

WEEKLY PLAN

01 02 03 04
05 06 07 08
09 10 11 12

TO DO LIST

MONDAY

TUESDAY

WEDNESDAY

THURSDAY

FRIDAY

SATURDAY

SUNDAY

PINKFOOT

WEEKLY PLAN

01	02	03	04
05	06	07	08
09	10	11	12

TO DO LIST

MONDAY

TUESDAY

WEDNESDAY

FRIDAY

PINKFOOT

WEEKLY PLAN

01 02 03 04
05 06 07 08
09 10 11 12

TO DO LIST

MONDAY

TUESDAY

WEDNESDAY

FRIDAY

SATURDAY

SUNDAY

PINKFOOT

ACCOUNT PAGE

DATE	CONTENTS	INCOME	OUTLAY	PAYMENT OPTION	TOTAL
				☐ CASH / ☐ CARD	
				☐ CASH / ☐ CARD	
				☐ CASH / ☐ CARD	
				☐ CASH / ☐ CARD	
				☐ CASH / ☐ CARD	
				☐ CASH / ☐ CARD	
				☐ CASH / ☐ CARD	
				☐ CASH / ☐ CARD	
				☐ CASH / ☐ CARD	
				☐ CASH / ☐ CARD	
				☐ CASH / ☐ CARD	
				☐ CASH / ☐ CARD	
				☐ CASH / ☐ CARD	
				☐ CASH / ☐ CARD	
				☐ CASH / ☐ CARD	
				☐ CASH / ☐ CARD	
				☐ CASH / ☐ CARD	
				☐ CASH / ☐ CARD	
				☐ CASH / ☐ CARD	
				☐ CASH / ☐ CARD	

DATE	CONTENTS	INCOME	OUTLAY	PAYMENT OPTION	TOTAL
				☐ CASH / ☐ CARD	
				☐ CASH / ☐ CARD	
				☐ CASH / ☐ CARD	
				☐ CASH / ☐ CARD	
				☐ CASH / ☐ CARD	
				☐ CASH / ☐ CARD	
				☐ CASH / ☐ CARD	
				☐ CASH / ☐ CARD	
				☐ CASH / ☐ CARD	
				☐ CASH / ☐ CARD	
				☐ CASH / ☐ CARD	
				☐ CASH / ☐ CARD	
				☐ CASH / ☐ CARD	

TOTAL......

INCOME....

OUTLAY....

CASH.......

CARD.......

ETC.........

PINKFOOT

DATE	CONTENTS	CHECK	DATE	CONTENTS	CH

FREE

MEMO

PINKFOOT

PINKFOOT

PINKFOOT

Paris, mon amour ♡

Coffee Paris

ELiER

PINKFOOT

PINKFOOT

PINKFOOT

PINKFOOT

PINKFOOT

PINKFOOT

PERSONAL
DATE

NAME

BIRTHDAY

MOBILE PHONE

E-MAIL

HOMEPAGE / SNS

DESIGNED AND PRODUCED BY PINKFOOT
WWW.PINKFOOT.CO.KR